SEVEN WAYS TO HELP YOUR CHILD WITH MATHS

CONTENTS

Dear Parents,

It is increasingly recognised that children helped by their parents do better at school than those who receive no help.

The National Curriculum is concerned with applying maths to practical tasks and real-life problems. It is essential that your child begins to learn mathematical concepts through practical activities, based on the world around him and as parents you have excellent opportunities in everyday situations to show that maths can be a tool and of real use. You can give him individual time and attention and help to make maths enjoyable, not something to be feared.

The following ideas will, I hope, show you how you can help your child.

Many of the items in the games and booklist are obtainable from school suppliers who also deal with private customers.

Barbara Geere   (Cert. Ed.)

The child is referred to as 'he' to avoid the awkward 'he/she'.

BY EXAMPLE

1

If you are interested then your child is more likely to be interested - so be positive in your attitude to maths. Don't say 'it's difficult' or 'it's boring' or 'I could never do it'.

Maths is often labelled as 'hard' and many adults are frightened at the thought of doing any but the most basic calculations. Fear of maths probably began with lack of understanding when they were very young.

We know that we understand and remember things better if we do or find out things for ourselves rather than just being told, and this is why it is important to start with practical experience.

Maths is usually associated with juggling with numbers and doing sums, but it is much more than this. We use maths to make life easier, to bring order to everyday situations, to solve practical problems. So involve your child in weighing flour for a cake, measuring up for a new fence, estimating how much the shopping will be etc.

But we can't expect a child to discover everything himself without constructive guidance. The maths we know has been built up over centuries of practice and thought and inspiration. This is why principles and rules which pass on this knowledge are an important part of maths.

If you have been worried by maths yourself you may find that you learn with your child and become more interested as you understand how he learns. You will also have given your child a positive attitude on which teachers can build.

SHOW THAT MATHS IS A TOOL

2

Maths is a way of bringing order and organisation into our lives. One way we do this is by using numbers and signs as symbols. At first, a child may see no connection between the shape of a number and the situation it stands for. He won't understand what 'two-ness' is until he begins to associate the shape 2 with two sweets or two bricks.

Draw his attention to how many bottles of milk you have each day, how many letters the postman delivers.

Start with small numbers up to 5 and point out examples around you.
His bike is a 3 wheeler or a 2 wheeler.
There are 4 legs on a chair/table.
Count the number of buttons on his coat.
Count aloud the number of stitches if you are knitting.
Count the ingredients when you are cooking, eg. 2 eggs, 4 spoonfuls of sugar.
Count out the number of sweets/apples you share out. He'll soon spot the difference here.

Now he can begin to understand what 2 or 3 is, just as we know what green means because we see lots of things given that name and begin to understand what 'green-ness' is. It is useful at this stage for him to begin to write or trace the shape of the numbers.

But maths is much more than counting and using numbers. Maths is also concerned with the relationships between things in size, shape, quantity and space and the way we use them in practical situations.

To begin with, **the language of maths is the language of everyday life.** Words like 'more', 'shorter', 'heavier', 'smaller', 'equal' are all basic mathematical vocabulary. So introduce situations where you can use these words.

MONEY

Your child will see you take coins from your purse but to begin with he may not see the link between them and the goods. He will gradually understand that some things cost **more** than others.

Let him handle the coins, looking at their design and size will help him to memorise them.

Make coin rubbings by placing a piece of thin paper over the different coins and rubbing a wax crayon across the surface.

Talk about what you can buy with the different coins. Let him help you to choose the right ones for small purchases. Give him a 5p coin to buy some sweets in a shop and then buy the same selection yourself and pay with 5 separate pence so that he can see that they have the same purchasing power.

MEASUREMENT

A height chart might show that he is **shorter** than Dad, **taller** than his little sister and **the same** as his friend. To begin with, he can measure with parts of his body - his feet, his stride, the span of his hand, his thumb. These, after all, were the first ways of measuring used by man. He can compare the size of items, eg. the toy lorry is 4 spans, the toy car is 3 spans. The pavement is 2 strides wide, the driveway is 4 strides wide.

Count how many steps there are between lamp posts in a road. Your steps and his will be different in size. He will begin to realise that it can be different for different sized hands or strides and that there is a need for standard measurement and from here he can be introduced to measuring with a tape or rule.

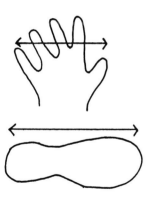

AREA
Use the words area and surface in everyday situations, eg. the grass area/ concrete area in the park; the working surface in the kitchen.
What size of tablecloth do we need to cover this table?
How much wrapping paper do we need for this present?
How much paint to cover the surface of the cupboard?
These are all practical problems which we have to work out reasonably accurately - mistakes can be costly.

Let him choose which cloth is needed for the table and if the table is extended, which cloth is then needed? Likewise, the sheet for a double bed needs to be bigger than one for a single bed.

Even by poking things into holes eg. plasticine or mud into cracks, he is learning about area and volume.

VOLUME AND CAPACITY
The volume of a container is how much space it takes up. The capacity of a container is how much it will hold, eg. the volume of a teapot is the amount of space it takes up in the cupboard. Its capacity is the amount of tea it will hold. How big a jug do you need to hold a pint/litre of milk? A small jug won't hold all of it and if you went on pouring, it would overflow. We know this by experience but it is something that small children find difficult to assess.

Water play at the sink or in the bath will allow him to experiment and find out.

Provide lots of different types of containers: tall and thin ones, small round ones, even sieves and colanders so that he finds out which will hold water.

Get him to talk about what he is doing and make sure that he understands words like 'empty', 'half-full', and 'overflowing'.

Ask him to estimate how many cupfuls would be needed to fill a jug or teapot. Then let him fill the jug or teapot in cupfuls, counting to see how close he is to his estimate. Emphasise that to be completely accurate the cups must be full to the brim and that he mustn't spill any.

Conservation of liquid. A pint of liquid remains a pint whether in a shallow saucepan or a tall bottle. Pour a pint of milk into a jug and then pour it back into the bottle to show that although it looks different it has stayed the same. Try other shapes of bottles or containers.
A sandtray also gives useful experience in finding out about volume and capacity - or try filling plant pots of differing sizes in the garden.

WEIGHT AND MASS
We have probably all been caught out at some time by the question: 'which is heavier, a pound of lead or a pound of feathers?' The fact that they weigh the same, each being a pound, can be difficult for a young child to grasp.
He knows from the feel of it that weight is 'pulling down'. While he is playing he will find out that some objects are heavier than others.

Encourage him to compare things using the words 'heavier, lighter'. He will soon discover that this depends on what you compare things with, eg. a pencil is heavier than a piece of wool but lighter than a potato.

Get him to talk about what he finds out using the mathematical vocabulary.

Look at the weights on food packages together. The need for standard weights can be introduced.
A pair of kitchen scales with weights is useful. **Let him experiment to see which items balance**, using toys, piles of buttons etc. Use the words 'balance', 'equal'.

Introduce the terms 'more than', 'less than'. He will probably derive great pleasure and satisfaction from getting the pans to balance. Introduce items which are heavier or lighter than they seem from their size, eg. a polystyrene tile, a latex cushion, a stone.

Get him to estimate what might balance with what. Weigh, say a pound of sugar against a pound of apples then replace the sugar with the metal pound weight to show that they are the same.
The see-saw is of course an excellent help in understanding weight, especially when a variety of different people are involved.

Conservation of mass. If an object changes shape eg. a block of plasticine is rolled out into a long thin shape, a young child will often assume that it has become 'more'. Test this on the scales with two equal blocks of plasticine (or anything else malleable). Take one block and roll it out into a different shape and then weigh again

TELLING THE TIME
This is, of course, another way of measuring and ordering. There are two aspects to learning about time:

1. Understanding the passing of time.
2. Learning to tell the time from a clock.

Time is abstract - you can't feel it or see it, if you are engrossed in something interesting it seems to go quickly.

An egg timer helps him to 'see time passing'. Use it to time events eg. 'can you be ready for bed before the timer runs out?'

For longer durations you can use a water clock (see activities).

Sowing seeds and bulbs and watching them develop will also help him to understand the passing of time.

Make opportunities to refer to time, eg. 'dinner is in ten minutes', 'see how many minutes it takes to put your toys away', 'can you do it more quickly?'

Get him to estimate how long it might take to complete a task.

What can he do in a minute?
How many times can he hop?
How many times can he bounce a ball?
How many strides can he take?
Time him and see how close his estimate is to what he actually does.

The pattern and sequence of events is another way of assessing time. Discuss the events of the day, eg. mealtimes and bedtime and link them with the times on the clock face.

Telling the time from the clock.
A clear clock face with moveable hands is needed. It is useful to have a mechanism. An old kitchen clock would be ideal (not one with Roman numerals).

It is necessary for the child to know the numerals 1-12 and to understand what is meant by halves and quarters.

Through practical experience a child begins to understand the usefulness of maths and is then more likely to be motivated to learn the principles and rules which will help him to solve problems more quickly.

DEVELOP ORDER AND PRECISION

3

Maths is an organised, structured subject. It is closely associated with order and pattern. These aspects occur naturally in children's play and you can encourage and develop them.

SORTING AND CLASSIFYING
This is the basis of logical thought. If we want to solve a problem we must first sort out what information we have.

Practice in sorting helps your child to order and classify. Let him sort a box of different items, eg. buttons, pegs, beads or pencils, putting them into separate piles.
Books can be sorted into different categories, eg. picture books, story books, poetry books, information books.

Tidying up provides lots of opportunities. Start with small numbers of items. Washing can be sorted into piles for the different machine programmes.
Put away toys in their different groups, eg. the bricks, the tea set, the dolls, the construction set.
Sort out crockery into piles of plates, saucers, bowls.

Ask him how many sorts of animals there are in his farm set and suggest that he organises them into smaller groups or sub sets, eg. the pigs, the sheep, the cows. When he is sorting his cars 'plant' a van or a bus with them and ask him which is odd man out and why?

Widen his experience by encouraging him to classify according to colour, shape or material, eg. wood, plastic, metal.

Widen his awareness of shapes by pointing out tiles that are square, clocks that are round, the varying shapes of playground apparatus.

ORDERING AND SEQUENCING

There are lots of toys available to practise these, eg. nesting cubes, Russian dolls. There are also many things around the house, eg. sets of saucepans, graded sizes of bowls. Through playing with these your child will learn the concepts of size, fit and serial order. The idea of ordinal number can be introduced eg. 1st, 2nd, 3rd (1, 2, 3, being the cardinal numbers).

MATCHING

A small child often thinks that he is counting just by reciting the number order 1, 2, 3 ... but, while it is a good thing for him to know the number sequence, if he says several numbers to one finger or one brick he is not understanding the mathematical connection and it is a meaningless chant.

It is essential that he matches a number to an item, so provide plenty of opportunities for him to practise the idea of matching 'one to one'.

Buttoning up his coat he will see that **one button matches one buttonhole.** Use 'as many as'.

Match one egg to one egg cup, one lid to one saucepan, one cup to one saucer.

Make the number of cups and saucers different so that there's an unequal number. This will introduce vocabulary like 'more than' and 'fewer than'.

Sequencing is useful to practise matching. He can thread beads in a simple pattern, eg. red/yellow/green/blue and then copy this on another thread.

Conservation of number. 6 bricks are the same whether they are scattered on the floor or piled one on top of each other, but young children often think that

the number of bricks has changed.
Help him to understand this by:
getting him to **match each brick with a square** on a strip of squared paper (start with small numbers first). Colour in one square for each brick then move the bricks and match them again with the same squares, to show that there is still the same number.

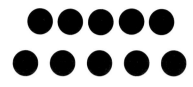

Place 5 counters in a row, then place another row of 5, more closely spaced, beneath this. Ask him if there are more, or fewer, or the same in each row. Count them.

We can determine number other than by counting. We recognise small arrays of dots in set patterns, eg. dominoes and dice.
Arrange counters in patterns of numbers, eg. ⦂ ⦂ or ∴ then re-arrange to show that however the counters are placed, they still remain the same number. Link with the equivalent number shapes by making cards which have the cardinal number (1,2,3,4 etc) and then the pattern of dots underneath. Dominoes and dice games are very useful for familiarising him with number patterns.

ADDITION
Dice can also be used for practising addition. Using two dice to begin with, he can add the dots each time they're thrown. At first, he will add the two numbers each time, but gradually he will remember the various number combinations (or number bonds) eg. 2 + 3 = 5, 7 + 3 = 10. Knowing number bonds is, like knowing multiplication tables, of great practical value and it is useful to practise these WHEN HE UNDERSTANDS WHAT HE IS DOING. (See back of book).

Provide more situations where he adds two lots of things together. He will discover that when **adding** numbers the order doesn't matter, eg. 6 + 3 = 9 and 3 + 6 = 9. This will be particularly useful when he deals with bigger numbers.

When faced with adding, say, 6 with 35, he can start with the bigger number and add on 6.

Introduce him to writing down the sum:

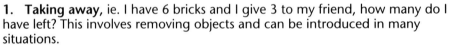

2 + 3 = 5

Move on to using larger numbers when you feel that he is ready.

SUBTRACTION

There are three aspects of subtraction.

1.   Taking away, ie. I have 6 bricks and I give 3 to my friend, how many do I have left? This involves removing objects and can be introduced in many situations.

I have 5 pence and pay out 3 pence. How many pence do I have left?
We take 4 pies from a batch of 6. How many pies do I have left?
A cake is cut into 8 pieces and we eat 4. How many pieces are left?

2.   Find the difference between two amounts. Matching is useful for understanding this.

If two children want to find out who has the most marbles, they need to know the difference. They can make two lines of the marbles, matching them up so that the difference becomes clear.

3.   Adding on. We use this in shopping situations. When we are given change by the shop assistant, having given, say, £1 for 70p worth of goods, she adds on as she puts the change into your hand . . . 80p, 90p, £1. Let your child hand over the money and receive change for you.

MULTIPLICATION

This is the repeated addition of groups or sets the same as each other.
When he meets with 2 + 2 + 2 + 2 + 2 + 2 and sees it as 6 lots of 2 he is
learning that multiplying is a quick way of adding numbers which are the same,
the multiplication sign, of course, being x. Thus 6 x 2.

Practise recognising groups of sets with the same number of items.
Animals go in 2's into the ark.
A place setting of knife/fork/spoon. How many lots of 3 for your family? How
many when there are visitors?
As with addition, the answer to two numbers multiplied together will be the
same whichever way round the number order, eg. 3 x 4 = 12 and 4 x 3 = 12.
He will discover this for himself if he sets the table for 4 people with knife/fork/
spoon and then sets it for 3 people with knife/fork/spoon/soup spoon.

DIVISION

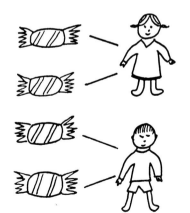

A child is often introduced to division by being asked to share items equally. To
begin with, he may give out the items randomly and find that some have more
than others. **Ask him how he can sort this out.**

Give him practice in sharing out different numbers of items. He will soon
realise that not every number can be shared equally in a group, ie. there will be
something left over when 3 or 5 or 7 sweets are shared between 2 children but
not if 4 or 8 are shared between 2 children.

Use the words 'share', 'between' 'equally'.
Another aspect of division is repeated subtraction - how many sets of 2 can I get
from 6?
Lay out 6 bricks/sweets etc. and subtract groups of 2.

ENCOURAGE IMAGINATIVE THINKING

4

Maths can easily become a dull, formal exercise if it is just the rigid application of rules and imposed methods. This is why imaginative and flexible thinking have an important part to play, particularly in problem solving. Even quite young children can invent strategies for solving problems, often unconventional but quite valid. They can be intuitive and have very agile minds.

So **encourage your child to think for himself** and have his own ideas about how to work something out. Later he can be shown that there may be a more efficient, standard way. **Encourage his curiosity and inquisitiveness** - ask him why - if he hasn't already asked!

Imaginative thinking doesn't mean muddle and imprecision.
Encourage methodical, ordered working out. Look for reasons and explanations which will lay the foundation for a logical, systematic approach.
Look for patterns and general rules eg. patterns and sequence in the multiplication tables.

He needs to be able to turn over ideas in his head and develop his concentration - games and activities which encourage this are useful.

He needs to be able to look at problems from different angles -literally, to begin with, eg. playing with shapes, fitting them together or into their appropriate holes, eg. posting boxes. This will be useful later on, in geometry.

Estimating and approximating is a good way of emphasising flexibility, so **encourage assessing of amounts** to be weighed, measured, counted or costed, then compare with the precise amount. It is also a help to know what sort of amount to expect - is the answer reasonable?

He needs to think with mathematical common sense, interpreting answers in practical terms, eg. the answer to the problem 'how many 2 seater bumper cars would you need to carry 5 people' is 3 not 2½.

Encourage him to enjoy playing with numbers:
how many sums can you make which add up to 10? eg. 5 + 5, 4 + 6. Try more difficult ways of making 10 eg:

1 + 2 + 3 + 4 = 10
or (4 x 2) + 4 - 2 = 10
or (3 x 4) - (1 x 2) = 10

Encourage him to see that **there isn't necessarily a right way and a wrong way** to arrive at an answer, eg. how many different ways can you think of for adding together two numbers, say 11 and 13?

1.   You can put 11 counters in a row and then put 13 more and count them all.

2.   You can take 1 off the 11 and add to the 13 making 14, then it is easy to add the remaining 10.

3.   Use tens and units columns
$$\begin{array}{r} 11 \\ + 13 \\ \hline 24 \\ \hline \end{array}$$

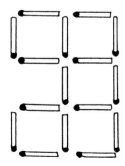

4.   Use tens and units by the linear method, eg.
     10 + 10 = 20
     then 1 + 3 = 4
     then add the totals
     20 + 4 = 24

Any more ideas?

Solving problems through practical examples provides a useful base for more abstract work later on. Many older children who find 'problem work' difficult aren't easily able to visualise the problem into parts - look at what you know and what you don't know.

Talk about problems together, try out ideas, guess, test, eliminate, adjust, conjecture.

Use games and activities which promote imaginative thinking:
Cuisenaire rods, Rubik cubes and pyramids, matchstick puzzles which require patterns to be made from a limited number of matchsticks.

It is important for your child to realise that maths can be a creative activity and is not a rigid body of knowledge which cannot be developed.

MAKE IT FUN
5

Make use of your child's natural enthusiasm, curiosity and enquiring mind so that **maths can be enjoyable and satisfying.**

Once one to one matching has been understood **use singing rhymes** to learn the sequence of number, eg.
1,2,3,4,5 once I caught a fish alive,
1 man went to mow . . . ,
10 green bottles. The end of this rhyme - 'no green bottles' is particularly useful in conveying the idea of 'nothing'.

Look at house numbers as you go down a road. Usually each side is numbered in odds and evens - useful for learning which is which, and good practice for counting in twos. What will the next number be?

Save empty cartons, yoghurt pots, etc. to set up a mini shop. **Get him to sort a pile of coins into separate values,** eg. 1p coins, 2p coins, etc. for practice at identification as well as for ease of giving change in his shop.
Point out that coins have a head and a tail side. Toss a coin when you play a game, to decide who is to go first. He'll soon recognise which side is which!

Pick up two sticks in the park and look at how they're alike and how they are different, eg. size, texture, weight, shape. Estimate how long they each are. Measure accurately when you get home to see whose estimate was the nearest.

Learn about area by drawing round different leaves on squared paper and counting how many squares they cover. Pastry cutters can be used instead of leaves.

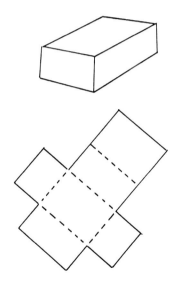

Explore the surface area of different shapes by unfolding a carton (cube or cuboid) and laying it flat. Do the same with Smarties tubes (cylinders), Pyramints (pyramids), etc. Do the reverse by making up a box out of a piece of card.

Use natural objects to build up multiplication tables, eg.
Sycamore seeds come in pairs - 2 x table,
Clover leaves come in threes - 3 x table,
Legs of animals come in fours - 4 x table etc.
Get him to suggest examples of objects to use for each number.

Estimating and approximating can be good fun as well as being invaluable practice.
How many people could we squeeze into the Wendy House?
How many of us could sit on a park bench?
How long would it take to run across the lawn/down the path?

Recognising patterns is a basic aspect of mathematics.
Make patterns with paints/crayons/felt tipped pens, etc., eg. /0/0/0/0/0/ or x-x-x-x-x- using shape and colour.
Look for patterns around you occurring naturally like flowers, leaves, shells, feathers, or man-made patterns such as wrought iron railings and gates, paving stones, wallpaper, curtains, crockery.

Recognising shapes - many popular toys are based on common geometric shapes, eg. the ball (a sphere), the drum (a cylinder), bricks (cubes and cuboids). The popular posting box toy has geometric shapes, made to fit into the holes in the lid.

Look out for shapes in shopping. By handling different shaped objects like Smarties tubes, cereal boxes, Toblerone bars, Pyramints, he will learn about cylinders, cuboids, prisms, pyramids. **Introduce the names of the shapes** as you meet them.

Hunt the shapes at home or when you go out for a walk, etc.
How many cuboids (tablets of soap, cupboards, shoe boxes) can you see?
How many cylinders (pillar boxes, tree trunks, telegraph poles) can you see?

Look out for circles, squares, rectangles, triangles in traffic roundabouts, manholes, windows, doors, road signs. Which shapes fit exactly, leaving no gaps? **Look out for examples** eg. tiled floor, brick wall.

Let him experiment with shapes to see which fit together exactly and which leave gaps. **Get him to draw round** say, a 50p coin, several times, on a piece of paper. Can he fit the shapes next to each other without leaving gaps?
Try a sugar cube, the end of a Toblerone carton, the end of a kitchen roll.

Recognising symmetry. This is a special property of pattern and shape. It possesses balance. Two sided symmetry is found in a shape or pattern which can be cut along its central line (axis) into identical halves.

Look out for examples, eg. a pair of semi-detached houses. If you live in one it is interesting if your child can visit the one next door which is the reverse in plan.
A butterfly is an example of two-sided symmetry - the body being the axis.

Make a symmetrical pattern - paint a blob of colour on a piece of paper and fold it while it is still wet.
Some shapes have more than one axis eg. snowflakes, stars.

Rotational symmetry balances on a point rather than an axis.
Look out for examples, eg. a windmill toy, symbols and trademarks, the Isle of Man symbol.

Computers. There are many computer games available which can make learning fun (see back of book). Abstract ideas are often more easily understood by playing games together, discussing strategies, solving problems.

Calculators. Once your child understands what he is doing in adding, subtracting, multiplying and dividing and knows the signs then a calculator is a useful tool to speed up the routine side of maths operations and encourage precision, although he needs to know if the answer is reasonable - he may have pressed the wrong button.

PRACTISE! PRACTISE! PRACTISE!

Once an idea has been understood it needs to be reinforced by practice. It is more important to widen your child's experience by lots of practice rather than trying to push him into more formal writing down of number too soon. Give him freedom initially to find his own method of solution. Lots of examples and practice at dealing with specific everyday situations will help him to generalise and see patterns and rules.

Practise recognition of shapes and values of numbers.
Begin with numbers 1-5 then, when he is completely familiar with these, introduce numbers 6-10 then 10-20 and so on.

Point out number shapes when you see them used, eg. house numbers, television buttons, telephone numbers.

Get him to trace or copy the numbers. To begin with, the numbers should be large and on plain paper, using a thick crayon or pencil which doesn't require the hand control to be too precise.

It is useful to practise reciting the names of numbers when he has understood the one to one correspondence.

Let him use money in real shopping situations, encouraging him to assess which coin he will need to give for a purchase and what change he will get.

Give him opportunities for using the tape measure, scales and measuring jug.

Estimating is useful - how much will the goods in the basket cost? Compare the estimate and the exact amount.

Let him help you with shopping, asking him to fetch different weights and measures of goods, eg. 1kg of rice or a 2 litre bottle of lemonade.

Telling the time. It is useful for him to have a watch with a face. Make situations when he can use it, ie. to remind you about something in five minutes time or to know when his TV programme is due.

Play games to increase his attention span. Short spells of activity are best to begin with, gradually extending these. Memory games such as Pelmanism are useful.

Saying numbers or ideas aloud helps him to attend and remember.

Very young children learn a great deal through physical handling and movement. But as they grow older their memories and powers of abstraction develop and they rely less on concrete experience., ie. they do less and think more. When he comes to more formal work and moves on to abstract maths operations then **techniques and rules and rote learning have their place.**

It is useful to memorise multiplication tables and number bonds to be able to give a quick response to a problem. However, some children do have trouble learning tables and as the idea is to save time it is pointless to force the issue and it can be counter productive. As he gets older **encourage him to work things out in his head.** Mental agility is a great practical asset. He won't always have paper, pens and calculators with him.

Speed tests - doing a set of problems or number bonds or tables in a limited time - is good for developing attention and practice for future exams.
He will probably need to use concrete examples until well into the Junior school and for some children, longer than that. It is important that he isn't forced onto the next stage before he is ready but on the other hand too much drilling and unnecessary repetition becomes boring and time wasting.

BUILD UP CONFIDENCE

7

Having confidence means believing in yourself so it is important that a child sees himself as someone who is able to achieve.

One of the biggest aids to confidence is **understanding what you are doing.**

Being able to express himself and know the vocabulary of maths is important. **Encourage him to explain what he is doing;** ask him questions, discuss with him.

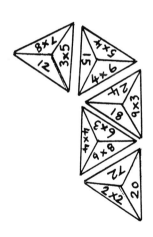

Use techniques and rules, having understood the basic concepts.

Being orderly and methodical is also important, **disciplining thoughts to give attention** to one thing at a time. This brings a feeling of being in control.

Checking the answer using a different method increases confidence.

Knowing tables and number bonds 'off by heart' is a tremendous confidence booster.

Bear in mind the **level of reading skills** of your child. Pre-readers, or ones who find reading difficult, need spoken rather than written instruction. Older children are often held back by lack of reading skills - more formal work often requires being able to read a work card or a book.

Estimating and approximating is useful - encourage him to have a go. Gradually he will become more accurate.

Practice reinforces all the above points.

Work as a team - not you as 'the one who knows' all the time. It is sometimes difficult to resist the urge to take over and 'show how it's done' rather than letting him work it out for himself. Don't immediately say 'no that's wrong' if he comes up with an inaccurate figure or suggestion - say 'have another think' and he will often correct himself.

However **sometimes 'showing' is appropriate.** Watch your own reactions and those of your child and you will learn how far his confidence and understanding will go and when to stand back and when to explain.
With an older child, past failures may have undermined his confidence. Go back

to easy examples of situations well within his understanding and then, as his confidence increases, move on to ones which require more effort.

Remember that **children learn as individuals** and need to go at their own pace.

CONCLUSION

Aim at a balance between guiding him and giving him freedom to explore, between investigation and memorising.

Provide him with opportunities for experimenting and solving problems.

Listen to him and talk over ideas to help him know what he means and understands. Generalisation will come when he has grasped the basic concepts.

It is important that he **enjoys what he is doing** and isn't unduly pressurised. If he's enthusiastic he will do the pushing. If he's interested he is more likely to concentrate and remember.

Practice leads to proficiency - he might not be so keen to practise tables but having this information 'at your fingertips' is of such practical value that it is well worth rehearsing them - say a few minutes a day, when he understands what he is doing.

Remember that **different children learn at different rates** - chronological age is not necessarily a guide to readiness for a new process.

Work together to learn. Enjoy 'bouncing ideas off each other'.

Develop method and order, using maths for everyday purposes, remembering that it is meant to be our servant not our master.

ACTIVITIES AND BOOKLIST

PRE- NUMBER ACTIVITIES

PRACTICE IN CLASSIFYING.
Investigate likenesses and differences between objects

Sort a box of counters/beads/cubes - get him to suggest how they can be put into groups or sets, eg.
a set of counters which are all the same size but different colours;
a set of beads which are of the same colour but different in shape;
a set of cubes which are all the same colour but of various sizes.
Soon he will realise that an object can have many different properties, eg. this bead has a hole, is blue and can roll, this cube has a hole but isn't blue and cannot roll.

Games to Buy
Counting Buttons   *Galt Educational N1713L*
Large 40mm easily handled plastic buttons, 4 colours and 4 different numbers of holes make them ideal for the early logic activities of sorting and grouping. Approximately 100 buttons in random selection.

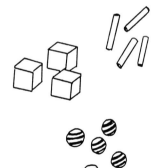

Set Attribute Dominoes   *Taskmaster T673*
24 plastic dominoes featuring pictures of ships which are linked according to colour, type, specific features. The game demands logical thought, keen observation and skill at selection and matching.

PRACTICE IN ORDERING AND SEQUENCING
Thread beads on a string in a simple pattern eg. red, blue, yellow, green. Copy the pattern using another string of beads.
Build two towers of coloured bricks, one copied from the colour sequence of the other.

Number Rummy
Remove the picture cards from a pack of playing cards. Each player is dealt

three cards and tries to build up a sequence, either by taking the top cards from the remaining unseen cards or by picking up the most recently discarded card. The winner is the first to make a sequence.

Games to Buy

Sequence Puzzles   *Learning Development Aids RP17*
Wooden puzzle pieces are specially cut and will only fit together in the right order. Gives practice in sequencing and logical thinking.

Sequence Tablets   *Galt Educational N1725C*
The 5 colours and 5 shapes give many opportunities for sorting, grouping, counting and sequencing and provide the means to create a range of perceptual and logic activities. 100 tablets - 4 of 5 shapes in 5 colours.

Pop'n Lock Beads   *Early Learning Centre*
Shape and colour sorting as well as sequencing.

Stacking Beakers   *Early Learning Centre*
For early grading games.

PRACTICE IN MATCHING

Pair familiar objects, eg. cup to saucer, knife to fork, lid to saucepan.

Let him set out cake papers for baking. one to each section of the bun tin.

Make a chart with pictures (pictograph) - one picture standing for one item to show how amounts of items compare, eg. 2 people with fair hair, 3 people with dark hair in the family.

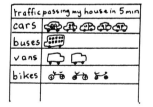

Stories like Goldilocks and the three bears provide useful examples of matching. Each bear has its own chair, porridge bowl, spoon, bed. **Draw pictures** of the three bears and allot the appropriate belongings to each one.

Games to buy

Lock up Garage   *Early Learning Centre*
Each of the three garages contains a car which matches the colour of the garage door.

Setting the Table   *Taskmaster T425*
Place mats in strong, washable plastic are patterned with a setting for knife, fork, spoon, plate, beaker for child to set correctly. Teaches table setting and one to one correspondence.

'Pond' Computer Game   *ESM Software ES645/ES345*
BBC Compact
Introduces to one to one correspondence, 'more than', 'less than', eg. 'Is there enough food for each bear?'. Easy to use - the games are exciting to play, with attractive pictures and jolly tunes which reward success.

ACTIVITIES WITH NUMBERS

When your child can recognise the numerals and understands counting, ie. matches one number to one item, then he needs lots of practice with using numbers.

Choose a number for the day and see how many items having that number of components can be seen, eg. a car with 4 wheels, a table with 4 legs.

Make a tray with compartments (or use an old cutlery tray) number each compartment 1, 2, 3 ... and adding, for extra help in identification, the appropriate amount of coloured dots by each number. He can then sort a collection of small objects into the compartments according to the number stated. The coloured dots can be removed when he no longer needs them to help him.

Draw or cut out pictures of a number of objects, eg. 4 dogs. Get him to count

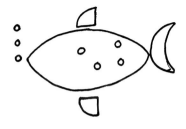

them and say how many there are, then write the numbers down. Reverse this, ie. write down a number and ask him to draw that number of dogs.

Make a fish game - you can make or buy many variations of this game. Draw a 'fish body' on a piece of paper. Using dice throw 1 to add 1 tail, throw 2 to add 2 fins, throw 3 to add 3 bubbles, throw 4 to add 4 spots. The numbers must be thrown in the correct order.

Bingo Make a set of cards with different selections of numbers - say 1-10. Put squares of paper marked with numbers 1-10 into a paper bag and call randomly. The first player to cover his card on all numbers is the winner. Check his card!

Playing cards provide ample scope for practising number recognition and counting.

Number Snap. Snap two adjacent cards with equal numbers regardless of colour or suit.

'More than' Remove 3 of the 'two' cards and share cards equally between 2 players. Each player plays a card from his unseen pile and the player with 'more than' the other claims both cards and places them at the bottom of his own pile.

'Fewer than' - remove 3 'ten' cards rather than 3 'twos'.

Number Pelmanism. Place a pack of playing cards (minus picture cards) face down on the table. Players take it in turn to try to turn up two cards with the same number of them.

Practice using ordinal number names, eg. First, second, third, etc. These names don't seem to have any connection with one, two , three . . . so create opportunities to make the connection clear.
'Who would like a **second** helping?' 'This is the **third** shop we've been to.'

PRACTISING ADDITION

Addition is combining sets or groups of items.

Count the number of items of shopping in the baskets. Put in 3 more packets. How many now?

Are there enough seats around the table now we have visitors? 4 dining room chairs + 3 bedroom chairs + 2 stools. Is that enough?

Dice and playing cards are useful for addition practice, either simple adding of two dice numbers thrown, or two cards picked up or as part of a game.

Track Game - Draw a simple track of squares on a large piece of paper, labelling one end as START and the other end as FINISH. Place matchboxes randomly on a number of the squares, some containing 1 counter, others empty. Each player is given 3 counters as stock and takes turns to throw a dice and move another counter along the track the required number of places. If he lands on a 'matchbox' square he can open the matchbox. If it contains a counter he collects it and adds it to his stock. If there is no counter in the box he must place one of his own there. After all the players have crossed the finishing line the one with the most counters is the winner.

Match That! - Two players each have an equal number of counters and take it in turns to throw a dice to indicate how many counters from their pile must be placed in the middle of the table. The other player must match that number with counters from his own pile and say how many the two sets of counters make altogether. If he is correct he wins all the counters. Play until one player runs out of counters. It may be necessary for an adult to be present either as player or adjudicator!

Spinning Tops - cut a regular hexagonal shape from a piece of card. The segments can be numbered and a pencil pushed through the centre. The top is spun round twice (later - three times) and the numbers at which the top comes

to rest each time are added together.
Scoring games such as skittles, tunnel ball, snooker.

PRACTISING SUBTRACTION

Subtraction is the reverse side of addition and this is made clear if a child starts with the whole and then sets aside a part of it, eg. a set of 10 crayons has 4 taken from it leaving 6. We can add the 4 back to the 6 to make the set of 10 again. Practise lots of situations like this.

Practise finding the difference between his pile of 12 Lego bricks and your pile of 7 by matching them in a line one to one. 'He has 5 more than you.' Look for lots of examples like this.

Fingers are convenient adding and subtracting apparatus of course - rhymes like 'Fly away Peter, fly away Paul, come back Peter, come back Paul' can be used to reinforce adding and subtracting.

Flannel Board - Glue a piece of flannel or baize or brushed nylon onto a piece of strong card. Make a collection of cut-out pictures glued onto card with a scrap of Velcro on the back. Use to practise adding and subtracting, eg. 4 pictures of flowers, take one away, how many now?

Postman Game - Your child could be postman with a bundle of 10 letters to deliver, using toys or visitors as recipients. Deliver 2 to Mrs. Jones. How many left? Deliver 4 to Auntie Jane. How many left now?

Spinning Tops - Make 2 regular hexagonal shapes from different coloured card, say, red and blue. Label segments of the red top with numbers 0-5. Label the blue one with numbers 5-10. Push a pencil through the centre of each. Spin the tops and where the top comes to rest, subtract the number on the red from the number on the blue.

PRACTISING MULTIPLICATION
Practise looking for equal sets
1 bird has two wings - 2 birds have 4 wings
1 stool has 3 legs - 2 stools have 6 legs
1 car has 4 wheels - 2 cars have 8 wheels

Use farm animals or toy cars or dolls to make equal sets. Make cages/garages/rooms and put the same number in each.
1 cage with 3 animals makes 3 animals
2 cages with 3 animals makes 6 animals
3 cages with 3 animals makes 9 animals, etc. (or use hoops and counters)
This is the beginning of a practical way of building up multiplication tables so that he understands what he is doing.

Look for examples of multiplication in shopping eg. egg cartons, groups of yoghurts, batches of rolls, crates of drinks.

How many pairs of shoes/gloves/socks in the wardrobe - good practice for counting in twos.

Once a child has understood multiplication through practical examples it is useful to practise multiplying numbers through games.

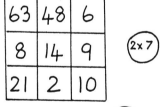
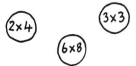

Multiplications Pairs Game - Make a pack of cards, each card having a number between 0-10 written on it. The pack should be shuffled and shared, face down, between two players. Each player turns over the top unseen card of his pile and the first player to say what the numbers make when multiplied together gets 1 point. The winner is the player with the most points when the cards have all been turned over once. It is useful to have multiplication tables to hand to use as adjudicator if necessary.

Bingo Tables. Multiplication version of this well known game, uses number multiplications, eg. answers from multiplication tables on the cards. The calling counters have multiplication sums instead of single numbers written on them. The players place their counters over the answer to the sum called, if it is on their card.

PRACTISING DIVISION

Division is the reverse side of multiplication and can be closely linked with it in games and activities.

Sort out a pile of socks - How many pairs? There are 5 pairs in a pile of 10 socks, the reverse being that 5 pairs make 10 socks.

Practise sharing sweets, etc. for the family/a group of children, in the appropriate number of piles/containers.

Arrange toys/people in a row behind a screen with just their feet showing. How many toys/people are there?
Once the concept of division is understood, a knowledge of multiplication tables is an invaluable aid to quick association of number links.

Bingo Tables - as described above, the calling counters having division sums written on them.

Racing Division - Use a set of cards, each one having a number between 0-10 written on it. Spread the cards face up on the table and ask the players to pick up a card which is the answer to a division sum you ask them, eg. 'what is 10 ÷ 2?' or 'how many 2's in 10?' They must pick up a 5 card. The first one to pick up the correct card wins a point. If there is only one player he could see how many correct answers he could make in a given time.

Games to buy

Numerical Jigsaws *Galt Educational GN0317G*
Each of the 10 numerals is cut into equivalent number of pieces and is of a different colour.

That's Right *Galt Educational N4405J*
Six games to help children understand numbers.

Cuisenaire Rods *E.J. Arnold SY358 R*

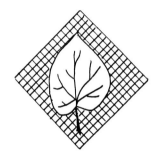

Tom Ten *Taskmaster T710*
A simple 'tens and units' game.

Solve-a-sum *Taskmaster T709*
A mental arithmetic game for juniors.

How Does Your Garden Grow? *Early Learning Centre*
An adding and subtracting game.

Multiplication Dominoes *Taskmaster T533*
Four sets of 'tables' dominoes in one box, printed in different colours for easy identification of the sets.

Division Shapes *Taskmaster T551*
Two division games boxed together, consisting of two sets of 24 plastic triangles. The problems are matched to the answers in domino fashion.

Coin Dice *Taskmaster T495*
Invent your own money games with this box of three extra large plastic dice bearing facsimiles of coins of each denomination.

Aspex Fractions *Philip & Tacey N153 1*
A set of self corrective matching cards presenting fractions in illustrated form as parts of common objects.

Clock Stamp *Taskmaster T702*
Rubber stamp showing digital and analogue faces.

First Squares *Philip & Tacey S596*
Each square has been halved in a different way so that the child must recognise the correct symmetrical pairs in order to reassemble all the squares.

Measuring Grids *Galt Educational N5561B*
For accurately assessing surface area of irregular shapes.

Simple Balance *Galt Educational GN3000A*
For teaching comparative weights

Water Timer *Galt Educational N4812A*
An ingenious method for demonstrating the concept of time.

CALCULATOR GAMES

Abacus Children's Calculator *Philip & Tacey N647*
The keys are large numbers and symbols. Easy to see and press.

Darts Countdown *E.J. Arnold SY188R*
Dice game based on darts. Work out your score on the dice and subtract it from your running total - first to reach zero is the winner.

Calculator Snooker   *E.J. Arnold SY308R*
Devised to familiarise child with using the calculator and to develop essential
skills in estimation and reasoned mathematical thought.

Calculator Activity Workcards   *E.J. Arnold 0560 23600X*
Present a range of exercises, problems, games and puzzles in a colourful, lively
format. The emphasis is on helping the child to understand the mathematical
processes he is using, encouraging him to estimate the answer before
undertaking the calculation.

COMPUTER GAMES

Number Games - for all BBC computers   *Taskmaster*
Alien Addition - practice in adding at speed.
Minus Mission - practice in subtracting at speed.
Meteor Multiplication - practice in multiplying at speed.
Demolition Division - practice in dividing at speed.

Number Puzzler   *E.S.M. Software E A503 BBC*
Improve mental arithmetic, encourage addition and subtraction in number
noughts and crosses game.

Puff   *E.S.M. Software ES649 BBC/ES349 Compact*
Find Puff and free him. Ideal for discussion, logical deduction, strategy and
problem solving.

Best Four Maths   *E.S.M. Software EA515 BBC/EA315 Compact*
Number puzzler - encourages accuracy in addition and subtraction.
Table Adventures - reinforces multiplication and factorisation.
Number Painter - speeds up mental arithmetic.
Squeeze - stretches the abilities of the more able.

BOOKLIST FOR CHILDREN

Count Me, Count Me Again	*Early Learning Centre*
Stile Early Maths	*L.D.A. LD585*
Real Things Number Book	*Philip & Tacey N521*
All About Ten	*Philip & Tacey N263*
Number & Picture Matching Strip Book	*Philip & Tacey N212*
Think & Solve - Mental Maths	Harold Clarke & Robert Shepherd, published *Cambridge Educational* (4 books in series)

BOOKLIST FOR PARENTS

Early Maths	Cynthia Dawes • *Longman*
Teaching Children Through the Environment	Pamela Mays *Hodder & Stoughton*
Structure in Early Learning	Alice Yardley • *Evans*
Let Me Count	Dorothy M. Jeffree • *Human Horizons Series*
Help Your Child with Maths	*B.B.C. Books*
Maths from 5 to 16	*Department of Education & Science H.M.S.O.*

WORKCARDS

Stile Maths Cards   *L.D.A. LT5*

Number - set of cards dealing with numbers up to 100, place value, addition, subtraction, multiplication, division, sets and fractions.

Time - colourful cards covering sequencing, before and after, months of the year, days of the week, time language, O'clock, half past, quarter to, and quarter past.

Money - lively exercises that deal with money values up to £1.

Multilink Activity Cards   *Galt Educational N5875 K*

Set 1 - pre-number work, set 2 - pre-number work and numbers up to 9, set 3 - number experience up to 20, set 4 - number experience up to 100.

TWO DIMENSIONAL SHAPES

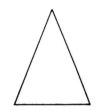

ISOSCELES TRIANGLE
2 sides of equal length

EQUILATERAL TRIANGLE
3 sides of equal length

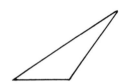

SCALENE TRIANGLE
No sides of equal length

SQUARE

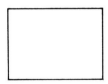

RECTANGLE

PENTAGON

HEXAGON

CIRCLE

THREE DIMENSIONAL SHAPES

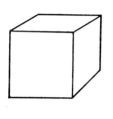

CUBE

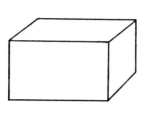

CUBOID

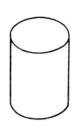

CYLINDER

SPHERE

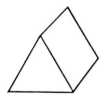

PRISM

CIRCLE BASED
PYRAMID

SQUARE BASED
PYRAMID

TRIANGLE BASED
PYRAMID

39

MULTIPLICATION TABLES

Practise when he understands what he is doing

2	3	4
0 x 2 = 0	0 x 3 = 0	0 x 4 = 0
1 x 2 = 2	1 x 3 = 3	1 x 4 = 4
2 x 2 = 4	2 x 3 = 6	2 x 4 = 8
3 x 2 = 6	3 x 3 = 9	3 x 4 = 12
4 x 2 = 8	4 x 3 = 12	4 x 4 = 16
5 x 2 = 10	5 x 3 = 15	5 x 4 = 20
6 x 2 = 12	6 x 3 = 18	6 x 4 = 24
7 x 2 = 14	7 x 3 = 21	7 x 4 = 28
8 x 2 = 16	8 x 3 = 24	8 x 4 = 32
9 x 2 = 18	9 x 3 = 27	9 x 4 = 36
10 x 2 = 20	10 x 3 = 30	10 x 4 = 40

5	6	7
0 x 5 = 0	0 x 6 = 0	0 x 7 = 0
1 x 5 = 5	1 x 6 = 6	1 x 7 = 7
2 x 5 = 10	2 x 6 = 12	2 x 7 = 14
3 x 5 = 15	3 x 6 = 18	3 x 7 = 21
4 x 5 = 20	4 x 6 = 24	4 x 7 = 28
5 x 5 = 25	5 x 6 = 30	5 x 7 = 35
6 x 5 = 30	6 x 6 = 36	6 x 7 = 42
7 x 5 = 35	7 x 6 = 42	7 x 7 = 49
8 x 5 = 40	8 x 6 = 48	8 x 7 = 56
9 x 5 = 45	9 x 6 = 54	9 x 7 = 63
10 x 5 = 50	10 x 6 = 60	10 x 7 = 70

8	9	10
0 x 8 = 0	0 x 9 = 0	0 x10 = 0
1 x 8 = 8	1 x 9 = 9	1 x10 = 10
2 x 8 = 16	2 x 9 = 18	2 x10 = 20
3 x 8 = 24	3 x 9 = 27	3 x10 = 30
4 x 8 = 32	4 x 9 = 36	4 x10 = 40
5 x 8 = 40	5 x 9 = 45	5 x10 = 50
6 x 8 = 48	6 x 9 = 54	6 x10 = 60
7 x 8 = 56	7 x 9 = 63	7 x10 = 70
8 x 8 = 64	8 x 9 = 72	8 x10 = 80
9 x 8 = 72	9 x 9 = 81	9 x10 = 90
10 x 8 = 80	10 x 9 = 90	10 x10 =100

NUMBER BONDS

Up to 5	Up to 10	Up to 20	
1 + 4 = 5	1 + 9 = 10	1 + 19 = 20	6 + 14 = 20
4 + 1 = 5	9 + 1 = 10	19 + 1 = 20	14 + 6 = 20
2 + 3 = 5	2 + 8 = 10	2 + 18 = 20	7 + 13 = 20
3 + 2 = 5	8 + 2 = 10	18 + 2 = 20	13 + 7 = 20
0 + 5 = 5	3 + 7 = 10	3 + 17 = 20	8 + 12 = 20
5 + 0 = 5	7 + 3 = 10	17 + 3 = 20	12 + 8 = 20
	4 + 6 = 10	4 + 16 = 20	9 + 11 = 20
	6 + 4 = 10	16 + 4 = 20	11 + 9 = 20
	5 + 5 = 10	5 + 15 = 20	10 + 10 = 20
	0 + 10 = 10	15 + 5 = 20	20 + 0 = 20
	10 + 0 = 10		0 + 20 = 20

ADDRESSES OF EDUCATIONAL SUPPLIERS

Free catalogues may be obtained from:

Learning Development Aids (L.D.A.)
Duke Street
Wisbech
Cambs. PE13 2AE
Tel: 0945 63441

ESM Software for Schools
Duke Street
Wisbech
Cambs. PE13 2AE

Galt Educational
Brookfield Road
Cheadle
Cheshire SK8 2PN
Tel: 061 428 8511

Philip & Tacey Ltd
North Way
Andover
Hants. SP10 5BA
Tel: 0264 332171

Taskmaster Ltd.
Morris Road
Leicester LE2 6BR
Tel: 0533 704286

E.J. Arnold Ltd.
Butterley Street
Leeds LS10 1AX
Tel: 0532 772112

Robert Gibson
17 Fitzroy Place
Glasgow G3 7BR
Tel: 041 248 5674

VTech Electronics
Electronic Learning
4 Blacklands Way
Abingdon Business Park
Abingdon
Oxon. OX14 1UE
Tel: 0235 555545

© Barbara Geere

Printed on Environment Friendly Paper by Print X Press, 11 Northend Trading Estate, Northend Road, Erith, Kent DA8 3PP